P9-CIV-321

STOCKING STUMPERS
TRIVIA EDITION

By S. Claus

RED-LETTER PRESS, INC.
Saddle River, New Jersey

Stocking Stumpers Trivia Edition

Revised and Updated 2009
Copyright ©2008 Red-Letter Press, Inc.
ISBN-10: 1-60387-106-3
ISBN-13: 978-1-60387-106-8

All Rights Reserved
Printed in the United States of America

For information address:

Red-Letter Press, Inc.
P.O. Box 393, Saddle River, NJ 07458
www.Red-LetterPress.com
info@Red-LetterPress.com

ACKNOWLEDGMENTS
SANTA'S SUBORDINATE CLAUSES

Editor:
Jack Kreismer

Contributors:
Russ Edwards, Jeff Kreismer, Kobus Reyneke

Cover & Page Design:
Cliff Behum

Typography:
Matt Taets

Introduction

Whether you're having a few quiet moments to yourself or enjoying a reunion with friends and family, Stocking Stumpers is the perfect holiday companion. Gather 'round the Christmas tree or simply kick back in your easy chair while trying out the holiday humdingers, tailor-made tests and trivia tidbits.

Once you've had a sampling, I think you'll agree, Stocking Stumpers is proof of the Christmas pudding that good things do come in small packages. Ho ho ho!

Merry Christmas!!!

S. Claus

The Mantle Meter

'Tis right around Christmas and
all through the book,

There are all sorts of stumpers
everywhere that you look.

There are quizzes and seasonal tests
to take you to task,

But what are those "stocking"
questions you ask?

Well, the stockings are hung
by the chimney with care.

The more that are filled,
the tougher the bear.

And so it is that
the Mantle Meter keeps score,

Rating the stumpers,
one stocking or more.

STOCKING STUMPERS

TRIVIA EDITION

FIRST THINGS FIRST

1.
Who was the first man in space?

2.
Who was the first vice president of the U.S.?

3.
What was the first fast food place in the U.S.?

4.
Levi Hutchins awakened the world
with what 1787 invention?

5.
Dubbed the "eighth wonder of the world"
when it opened in 1965, it was baseball's
first indoor stadium. Can you name it?

What did Eliot and Ruth Handler create in 1959?
(HINT: Santa's been bringing them to good little girls ever since.)

IF YOU LIKE TO ENGAGE IN MANY SESQUIPEDALIANISMS,
YOU LIKE TO USE BIG WORDS.

ANSWERS

1.

Soviet Army Major Yuri Gagarin, on April 12, 1961

2.

John Adams, in 1789

3.

White Castle, in Wichita, Kansas, in 1921

4.

The first alarm clock

5.

The Houston Astrodome

The Barbie Doll

IT WASN'T UNTIL THE CIVIL WAR THAT SPECIFIC LEFT AND RIGHT SHOES WERE MADE.

A Matter of Seconds

1. Statistics show that Cinco De Mayo is the biggest day for Americans to eat avocados. Can you tackle the second biggest avocado-eating occasion?

2. Who is second to Barry Bonds on Major League Baseball's all-time home run list?

3. Delaware became the first state in the U.S. Which state was second?

4. Before 1900, the Eiffel Tower, at 984 feet, was the world's tallest building. What was second?

5. What is second to the Nile (4,145 miles) as the world's longest river?

What's the most common last name initial in the United States?

THE LONGEST RECORDED LIFE SPAN OF A CAT IS 34 YEARS.

ANSWERS

1.

Super Bowl Sunday

2.

Hank Aaron, with 755 homers

3.

Pennsylvania

4.

The Washington Monument- 555 feet

5.

The Amazon (4,007 miles)

"S"

❄ SEASONAL STUMPER ❄

In what country did the poinsettia originate?

Mexico

ALPHABET SOUP

1. E is the most often used letter of the English alphabet. What letter is second in terms of frequency?

2. A, E, H, I, K, L, M, N, O, P, U and W are of what significance in Hawaii?

3. What does S.P.E.B.S.Q.S.A. stand for?

4. What does the "J.C." in JC Penney stand for?

5. What three-letter word is the last entry in the Random House Unabridged Dictionary, Second Edition?

What's the most visited home in the United States?

LESS THAN HALF OF THE SINGLE MEN IN THE U.S. WHO'VE REACHED THE AGE OF 35 EVER GET MARRIED.

ANSWERS

1.

The letter T

2.

They are the twelve – and only twelve – letters
of the Hawaiian alphabet.

3.

The Society for the Preservation and Encouragement
of Barbershop Quartet Singing in America

4.

C as in Cash, James Cash Penney, that is.

5.

Zzz, defined as "the sound of a person snoring"

The White House – Second is Graceland, the former
home of Elvis Presley, in Memphis, Tennessee.

JERRY SEINFELD SOLD LIGHT BULBS BY TELEPHONE.

WHAT'S UP?

1. What does the Christian acronym WWJD stand for?

2. What's Bugs Bunny's favorite expression?

3. What are Winnie the Pooh's first words when he wakes up in the morning?

4. What's the title of the feline song recorded by Tom Jones?

5. What is the name of the second baseman in Abbott and Costello's *Who's on First?* routine.

The microwave oven is used more for reheating what product than for any other reason?

THE AVERAGE AMERICAN EATS MORE LETTUCE THAN ANY OTHER VEGETABLE, AN AVERAGE OF 27.4 POUNDS PER YEAR.

ANSWERS

1.
What Would Jesus Do?

2.
"What's up, Doc?"

3.
"What's for breakfast?"

4.
What's New, Pussycat?

5.
That wasn't a question; it was a statement.
What is the second baseman in the skit.

Coffee

EMPLOYEES AT DISNEY WORLD WERE NOT ALLOWED
TO WEAR MUSTACHES UP UNTIL 2000.

MARQUEE MONIKERS

Match the stage name to the real name.

1. Jason Alexander

(a) Lawrence Harvey Zeiger

2. Larry King

(b) Reginald Dwight

3. Jamie Foxx

(c) Eric Bishop

4. Meatloaf

(d) J. Scott Greenspan

5. Elton John

(e) Marvin Aday

Are there more red stripes or white stripes on the U.S. flag?

JACK NICHOLSON SINGLE-HANDEDLY RESCUED
FIVE DROWNING PEOPLE FROM THE NEW JERSEY
SURF BACK IN THE 1950s.

ANSWERS

1. D

2. A

3. C

4. E

5. B

Reds win, 7-6.

❄ SEASONAL STUMPER ❄

Who wrote the Christmas classic, *The Gift of the Magi*?

O. Henry

By the Numbers

1.
How many toes do cats have?

2.
Name the Seven Dwarfs in the Walt Disney movie.

3.
In 1920, what amendment to the U.S. Constitution gave women the right to vote?

4.
How many of the first thirteen states of the U.S. can you name?

5.
Just how many karats is pure gold, anyway?

Within three, how many hot dogs did Joey Chestnut eat in 10 minutes in 2009 to set a new world record?

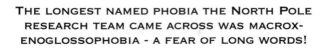

THE LONGEST NAMED PHOBIA THE NORTH POLE RESEARCH TEAM CAME ACROSS WAS MACROX-ENOGLOSSOPHOBIA - A FEAR OF LONG WORDS!

ANSWERS

1.

18- Five on the front paws, four on the back.

2.

Dopey, Sneezy, Grumpy, Happy,
Bashful, Doc, and Sleepy

3.

The 19th

4. Delaware was first, followed by Pennsylvania,
New Jersey, Georgia, Connecticut, Massachusetts,
Maryland, South Carolina, New Hampshire, Virginia,
New York, North Carolina, and Rhode Island.

5.

24K

LITTLE KNOWN LAW: IT'S ILLEGAL FOR A WOMAN
TO DRESS AS SANTA IN MINNESOTA.

FA LA LA LA LA

True or False?

1.

Irving Berlin wrote *White Christmas*.

2.

Jingle Bells was originally called
One-Horse Open Sleigh.

3.

O Christmas Tree originated in Belgium.

4.

If you received all the presents from the *Twelve Days of Christmas*, you'd get a total of 12 gifts.

5.

The writer of *All I Want for Christmas is My Two Front Teeth* was inspired by a toothless photo of hockey great Maurice Richard.

What does the "B.F." in B.F. Goodrich stand for?

ALBERT EINSTEIN NEVER WORE SOCKS.

ANSWERS

1.

TRUE

2.

TRUE- It was composed in 1857 by James Pierpont.

3.

FALSE- It was in Germany.

4. FALSE- The key word is *all* the presents. The true count would be 364 and since a lot of them were birds, you'd better find a good carpet cleaning service.

5. FALSE- In 1944, music teacher Donald Yetter Gardner was inspired to write the song when he noticed that most of his grade school students had at least one tooth missing.

Benjamin Franklin

HARRISON FORD HAS A SPECIES OF SPIDER,
CALPONIA HARRISONFORDI, NAMED AFTER HIM.

ARE YOU GAME?

1.
Parker Brothers introduced Monopoly in:
a) 1928 b) 1935 c) 1949 d) 1959

2.
If you were to add up all of the numbers in a single
Sudoku puzzle, what would be their sum?

3.
Ransom A. Treasure, Basil O. Cash, Cyrus Bonanza
and Hesperia Mint are all currency portraits appear-
ing on the play money of what board game?

4.
In which game do you answer questions in order to
collect "a piece of the pie"?

5.
An age-old board game, it was also the name of
Richard Nixon's pet cocker spaniel.
Name it.

On what day is Superman's birthday?

PINK LEMONADE WAS CREATED IN 1857
BY PETE CONKLIN, WHO UNWITTINGLY USED
A BUCKET OF WATER IN WHICH A CIRCUS
PERFORMER HAD SOAKED HIS RED TIGHTS.

ANSWERS

1.
B

2.
405

3.
Life

4.
Trivial Pursuit

5.
Checkers

February 29th

DIAMONDS ARE FLAMMABLE - BUT ONLY AT TEMPERATURES HIGHER THAN 1400 DEGREES FAHRENHEIT. TALK ABOUT HOT ROCKS!

IT'S ABOUT TIME

1.
Who first suggested the idea of daylight-saving time?

2.
What's the longest month of the year?
(Big hint: See question 1.)

3.
Who was *Time* magazine's Man of the Year for 1938?

4.
What's the term used for a man in need of a shave?

5.
How many times a day do the hands
of a clock cross each other?

What seven letters in the English alphabet
can double as Roman numerals?

FAIRY TALE WRITER HANS CHRISTIAN ANDERSON
WAS DYSLEXIC. OTHERS AFFLICTED BY DYSLEXIA
INCLUDE THOMAS EDISON, WOODROW WILSON,
TOM CRUISE AND HENRY WINKLER.

ANSWERS

1.
Ben Franklin

2.
October- Setting the clock back gives the 31-day month an extra hour.

3.
Adolf Hitler

4.
Five o'clock shadow

5.
22- They cross at 12:00, 1:05, 2:11, 3:16, 4:22, 5:27, 6:33, 7:38, 8:44, 9:49, and 10:55 (a.m. & p.m.).

I, L, V, D, X, C, and M

ACCORDING TO *FAST FOOD NATION*, THE AVERAGE AMERICAN WILL EAT 3 HAMBURGERS EACH WEEK.

MY WORD

Ho ho ho- you may have a few choice words for Santa after trying this quiz. Chances are you'll wind up in a Funk...and Wagnalls!

1. What two fifteen-letter words are spelled exactly the same except for the first letter?

2. What is alphabetically unique about the words unnoticeably, uncomplimentary and subcontinental?

3. There are only three words in the English language which end in "ceed". Can you name them?

4. What two five-letter words end with the letter "y" and do not contain the vowels a, e, i, o, or u?

5. Two words begin and end with the letters "und". One is underfund. What's the other?

What's the only animal that's eaten before it is born and after it is dead?

ROCKER ROD STEWART WAS ONCE A GRAVEDIGGER.

ANSWERS

1.
Rationalization and nationalization

2.
They each contain all the vowels in reverse order.

3.
Exceed, proceed and succeed

4.
Pygmy and gypsy

5.
Underground

A chicken

❄ SEASONAL STUMPER ❄

How many female reindeer does
Santa use to pull the sleigh?

Just one – Vixen.

THINKING BIG

1. What company is nicknamed "Big Brown"?

2. Do you know the stage name of rock 'n' roll singer J.P. Richardson?

3. He's a member of the warm-blooded egg-laying vertebrate family and is seen on a popular children's television show. Name him.

4. What Triple Crown-winning racehorse was nicknamed "Big Cy"?

5. "Big Salt Lick" was the original name of what city?

This city of the same name is the largest city in two different states. Name it.

LEAVE IT TO BEAVER WAS THE FIRST TV PROGRAM
TO SHOW A BATHROOM AND A TOILET.

ANSWERS

1. United Parcel Service, for its fleet of brown trucks

2. Big Bopper

3. Big Bird

4. Citation

5. Nashville, Tennessee

Portland (Maine and Oregon)

YES, THERE IS A HAMBURGER HALL OF FAME, AND IT'S LOCATED IN SEYMOUR, WISCONSIN.

BARKING UP THE CHRISTMAS TREE

1. Always one of the grandest displays in the world, when did the Rockefeller Center Christmas tree tradition start?
   a) 1903 b) 1913 c) 1923 d) 1933

2. What President began the National Christmas Tree Lighting Ceremony?
   a) Herbert Hoover   b) Calvin Coolidge
   c) Dwight Eisenhower   d) Gerald Ford

3. What's the most popular type of Christmas tree in the United States?

4. What's the only Christmas decoration ever banned by the government?

5. Do you know the German title of *O Christmas Tree?*

What do the letters LED on a digital watch stand for?

THE AVERAGE ADULT IN THE UNITED STATES
READS JUST 24 MINUTES A DAY.

ANSWERS

1.

D

2.

B- Calvin Coolidge, in 1923... The ceremony is now held on the White House lawn every year.

3.

Scotch pine, primarily because the needles, for the most part, stay on even after the tree becomes dry.

4.

Tinsel... It used to contain lead which is very poisonous. Nowadays, it's made of plastic and the worst you can get from it is a bad case of tinselitis...Ho ho ho!

5.

O Tannenbaum

Light-emitting diode

ACCORDING TO *HARPER'S INDEX,* 80 PERCENT OF AMERICANS BELIEVE IN MIRACLES.

PHRASE CRAZE

Here are some trivial messages that Santa's elves scrawled on the frosted workshop windows for you to solve. (Example: CCCCCCC= The Seven Seas)

1.
GSGE

2.
PE/A SOUP

3.
MIND
MATTER

4.
W O R D S
W O R D S

5.
STAND TAKE   TO   TAKING
I   YOU   THROW   MY

George Washington, the "Father of Our Country," had how many children?

THE AVERAGE AMERICAN HAS A
10,000 WORD VOCABULARY.

ANSWERS

1. Scrambled Eggs (FACT: *Scrambled Eggs* was the original title for the Beatles' hit song *Yesterday*.)

2. Split Pea Soup (FACT: Regarding soup, bird's nest soup really is from a bird's nest. In China, this delicacy is made from the Asian swift's nest.)

3. Mind Over Matter (FACT: One of the greatest minds of all time, Albert Einstein, was offered the presidency of Israel in 1952 but turned it down saying, "I know a little about nature, and hardly anything about man.")

4. Crosswords (FACT: Newspaper editor Arthur Wynne published the first crossword puzzle in America in the *New York World* on December 21, 1913.)

5. I Understand You Undertake to Overthrow My Undertaking (FACT: Speaking of undertakers, did you know that during the Civil War times, they were referred to as "Doctor"?)

0

❄ SEASONAL STUMPER ❄

What Christmas song, written by Jay Livingston and Ray Evans, was introduced in the 1951 movie *The Lemon Drop Kid* starring Bob Hope?

Silver Bells

MISCELLANEOUS MINDBENDERS

1. Four common words in the English language contain the consecutive letters N-A-C-L. How many can you name?

2. What U.S. city has the most lawyers?

3. Three different numbers give the same result when added together as when multiplied. What are they?

4. True or false? The facial hair we call sideburns got its name from a Civil War Union general who wore them, Ambrose Burnside.

5. How many keys are on a piano?

What's the only one of the Great Lakes that is entirely in the U.S.?

GUINNESS SAYS THE WORLD'S HARDEST TONGUE TWISTER IS THIS: "THE SIXTH SICK SHEIK'S SIXTH SHEEP'S SICK."

ANSWERS

1.

Barnacle, manacle, pinnacle, and tabernacle

2. Washington, D.C. ... That reminds the Stocking Stumpers crew of a riddle: An honest politician, a kind lawyer and Santa Claus are getting off an elevator when they spot a ten dollar bill. Who gets to pick it up? Santa Claus, of course. The other two aren't real.

3.

1, 2, 3

4.

True

5.

88- 52 white and 36 black

Lake Michigan – The other four all border on Ontario, Canada.

"CHOP SUEY" MEANS "ODDS AND ENDS".

I - OPENERS

The answers to the following all begin with the letter I as in "I'm dreaming of a white Christmas..."

1. It was his opening line as the original host of the "Weekend Update" segment of *Saturday Night Live.*

2. What sporting facility has the largest seating capacity in the world?

3. It was the catchphrase used by Lily Tomlin in her comedy routines as telephone operator Ernestine.

4. The letter "i" appears six times in what word?

5. What does the Latin word "veto" mean?

A "firkin" is how many pounds of butter?

THE AVERAGE AMERICAN LAUGHS
FIFTEEN TIMES A DAY.

ANSWERS

1.
   "I'm Chevy Chase and you're not."

2.   Indianapolis Motor Speedway (with a permanent
     seating capacity of over 257,000 people and infield
     seating that raises it to an approximate 400,000)

3.
   "Is this the party to whom I am speaking?"

4.
                      Indivisibility

5.
                      "I forbid"

56

EDGAR ALLAN POE OFTEN WROTE HIS WORKS
WITH HIS CAT SEATED ON HIS SHOULDER.

Seeing Stars

1. Name the television reality show based on the British series *Strictly Come Dancing*.

2. What is the nickname of the flag of the Confederate States of America?

3. Do you know the Green Bay Packers quarterback who was the MVP of the first two Super Bowls?

4. What chain opened its first retail store in Seattle's Pike Place Market in 1971?

5. The Singing Cowboy has the most stars on the Hollywood Walk of Fame, five (for five different entertainment categories). Can you name him?

How many numbers are there on a Bingo card?

U.S. PAPER CURRENCY MEASURES
6 1/8 BY 2 9/16 INCHES.

ANSWERS

1.
Dancing with the Stars

2.
Stars and Bars

3.
Bart Starr

4.
Starbucks

5.
Gene Autry

24

ALLIGATOR SHIRTS HAVE CROCODILES ON THEM.

COMMON CENTS

1. How many ridges are on a quarter?
   a) 1 b) 50 c) 119 d) 1776

2. Which lasts longer in circulation,
   the average coin or the dollar bill?

3. What's the most amount of change you could have
   without being able to make change for a dollar bill?

4. Of the penny, nickel, dime and quarter, which is the
   only one where the "head" is facing to the right?

5. True or false? The original motto on
   U.S. coins was "Mind Your Business."

What pet did Gary Dahl introduce in 1975?

AL CAPONE CARRIED A BUSINESS CARD STATING
THAT HE WAS "A SECOND HAND FURNITURE DEALER."

ANSWERS

1.

C

2. The average coin circulates for 15 to 20 years while the life span of a dollar bill is approximately 22 months according to *Forbes* magazine.

3.

$1.19- Three quarters, four dimes and four pennies

4. Honest Abe Lincoln, on the penny, is the only one facing right.

5.

True

The pet rock

❄ SEASONAL STUMPER ❄

If you were born on Christmas Day, what would your astrological sign be?

Capricorn

HOLIDAY HUMDINGERS

1. It began as an old English custom called Wassailing. What do we know it as today?

2. Do you know what Grandma happened to be drinking when she got run over by a reindeer?

3. In 1875, Louis Prang introduced a custom to America that is still popular to this day. Any idea what it is?

4. Instead of stockings, what is it that Swedish children put out for Santa Claus to leave goodies in?

5. What was Clement Moore's *The Night Before Christmas* originally called?

A marathon is 26 miles and how many yards?

THE LIFE SPAN OF A BASEBALL IN A MAJOR LEAGUE GAME IS SEVEN PITCHES.

ANSWERS

1.
Caroling

2.
Eggnog

3.
He began the tradition of sending Christmas cards.

4.
A wooden shoe

5.
A Visit from St. Nick

HOME PLATE IN BASEBALL WAS SQUARE UNTIL 1900 WHEN IT WAS MADE FIVE-SIDED TO HELP UMPIRES IN CALLING BALLS AND STRIKES.

COVER TO COVER

1. In 1996 and 2000, this athlete appeared on the cover of *Sports Illustrated* as Sportsman of the Year. He's the only one to win the award twice.

2. Who's the only person to appear on the cover of *TV Guide* three weeks in a row? (Hint: The year was 1991. Bigger hint: He moved into a little house after doing some bonanza stuff- all on his highway to heaven.)

3. Who was the cover feature of *People* magazine's first edition in 1974?

4. Norman Rockwell illustrated 317 covers over a 47 year period for what magazine?

5. He appeared on more than one cover of *Time* and, in fact, was named as the magazine's "Person of the 20th Century". Who is he?

How many pages does a standard U.S. passport have?

IF YOU SUFFER FROM POLYDACTYLISM, YOU HAVE MORE THAN YOUR FAIR SHARE OF FINGERS OR TOES.

ANSWERS

1.
Tiger Woods

2.
Michael Landon

3.
Mia Farrow

4.
The Saturday Evening Post

5.
Albert Einstein

MELT AN ICE CUBE IN YOUR MOUTH AND
YOU'LL BURN OFF 2.3 CALORIES.

ON A FIRST NAME BASIS

1. What's the real first name of actor Robert Redford, singer Pat Boone and baseball legend Casey Stengel?

2. What is Paul McCartney's first name?

3. Do you know salsa singer Marc Anthony's first name? And, for extra credit, what's his real last name?

4. Garth, as in the singer Brooks, is his middle name. What's his first name?

5. What is actress Jodie Foster's real first name?

How many hearts are there on the 6 of hearts?

THE SECOND MAN TO WALK ON THE LUNAR
SURFACE WAS BUZZ ALDRIN. HIS MOTHER'S
MAIDEN NAME IS MOON.

ANSWERS

1.
Charles

2.
James

3.
His real full name is Antonio Marco Muniz.

4.
Troyal

5.
Alicia

8

❄ SEASONAL STUMPER ❄

In the *Home Alone* holiday flicks,
who portrayed Kevin McCallister?

Macaulay Culkin

THE GAMES PEOPLE PLAY

*The game here is simple enough - match
the hobbyist with the hobby.*

1. Deltiologist   (a) Cigar band collector

2. Spelunker   (b) Banknote collector

3. Lepidopterist   (c) Postcard enthusiast

4. Notaphile   (d) Moth & butterfly devotee

5. Bandophile   (e) Cave explorer

Do you know the only number that is
twice the sum of its digits?

SMOKEY BEAR IS THE ONLY ONE IN AMERICA
WITH HIS OWN ZIP CODE- 20252.

ANSWERS

1.
C

2.
E

3.
D

4.
B

5.
A

18

PEPTO BISMOL, WHEN INTRODUCED IN 1901,
WAS CALLED MIXTURE CHOLERA INFANTUM.

THE ONE AND ONLY

1.
What's the only state with a one-syllable name?

2.
Quick- what's the only four-letter word that ends in "eny"?

3.
What's the only sport where the defensive team has the ball?

4.
What is the only number that can be added to itself or multiplied by itself with the same result?

5.
Can you name the only female animal with antlers?

What's the only state that ends with the letter "k"?

POTATO CHIPS WERE INVENTED IN 1853 IN SARATOGA, NEW YORK, BY GEORGE CRUM.

ANSWERS

1.

Maine

2.

Deny

3.

Baseball

4.

2 (2 x 2 = 4 or 2 + 2 = 4)

5.

This should have been an easy one...
After all, this is *Stocking Stumpers* – A reindeer.

New York

ELEPHANTS CAN SWIM VERY WELL. THEY JUST
HAVE TROUBLE KEEPING THEIR TRUNKS UP.

SCREEN TEST

1.

What woman has hosted the
Oscars the most times?

2.

Frasier, Joey and *Rhoda* were sitcoms that were
spinoffs from what other sitcoms?

3.

What does ESPN stand for?

4.

Who created the James Bond character?

5.

What's the longest-running
game show in TV history?

What's Donald Duck's middle name?

DALMATIAN DOGS ARE PURE WHITE
WHEN THEY'RE BORN.

ANSWERS

1.
Whoopi Goldberg, 4

2.
Cheers, Friends and *The Mary Tyler Moore Show*, respectively

3.
Entertainment Sports Programming Network

4.
Author Ian Fleming

5.
The Price Is Right, continuously since 1972

Fauntleroy

3% OF AMERICANS HANG FAMILY PICTURES IN THEIR BATHROOMS.

Affairs of State

1. The least populous state in the U.S. is:
   a) Montana   b) Wyoming
   c) Rhode Island   d) California

2. In what state is the geographic center of North America?

3. The forget-me-not is, fittingly, the state flower of …?

4. At Four Corners, you can walk in four states within a few seconds. Can you name those states?

5. Mt. McKinley is the highest peak in the United States. In what state is it located? And, for extra credit, what was the highest peak in the U.S. before Mt. McKinley was discovered?

Who was *Time* magazine's "Man of the Year" in 1982?

WOMEN SHOPLIFT MORE OFTEN THAN MEN
BY A RATIO OF 4 TO 1.

ANSWERS

1.

B

2.

North Dakota, in Pierce County

3.

Alaska

4.

Arizona, Colorado, New Mexico and Utah

5. Alaska- As for the second part to that question, well, that was a bit of Christmas chicanery. The highest peak before Mt. McKinley was discovered was- Mt. McKinley! It just hadn't been discovered yet.

The computer

TWEETY PIE WAS ORIGINALLY A PINK CANARY, BUT CENSORS COMPLAINED THAT HE LOOKED NAKED SO HIS COLOR WAS CHANGED TO YELLOW.

Initial Release

*Provide the title of the movie based on the initials,
then match the Oscar winner with it.*

1. TSOTL   (a) Tom Hanks

2. G   (b) Louise Fletcher

3. BH   (c) Jodie Foster

4. OFOTCN   (d) Russell Crowe

5. FG   (e) Charlton Heston

How many signs of the Zodiac are there?

ASPIRIN WAS INVENTED IN GERMANY IN
1853 BUT NOT MARKETED UNTIL 1899.
TAKE TWO AND CALL ME IN 46 YEARS!

ANSWERS

1.
C (*The Silence of the Lambs*)

2.
D (*Gladiator*)

3.
E (*Ben-Hur*)

4.
B (*One Flew Over the Cuckoo's Nest*)

5.
A (*Forrest Gump*)

12

HORSE RACING LEGEND MAN O' WAR
HAD A BAD MARE DAY WHEN HE SUFFERED
HIS ONLY DEFEAT- TO A HORSE NAMED UPSET.

TOTAL RECALL

See if you can identify what the following mnemonics help to recall.

1.
HOMES

2.
Every Good Boy Does Fine

3.
Roy G. Biv

4.
My Very Earnest Mother Just Served Us Nine Pickles

5.
Please Excuse My Dear Aunt Sally

What's the only number that has the
same number of letters as its name?

THERE ARE NO PENGUINS AT THE NORTH POLE.
ALL VARIETIES OF PENGUINS ARE FOUND BELOW
THE EQUATOR, MAINLY IN ANTARCTICA.

ANSWERS

1. H.O.M.E.S. is for the Great Lakes- Huron, Ontario, Michigan, Erie and Superior.

2. The first letters help to recall the musical notes of the treble-clef line, E,G,B,D,F.

3. Good ol' Roy G. Biv gives you a hand in remembering the colors of the rainbow – red, orange, yellow, green, blue, indigo, violet.

4. This was the way to remember the order of the planets – Mercury, Venus, Earth, Mars, Jupiter, Saturn, Uranus, Neptune and the former planet Pluto.

5. This is the order of operations in math- parentheses, exponents, multiplication, division, addition,and subtraction.

4

❄ SEASONAL STUMPER ❄

The Twelve Days of Christmas covers what period of time?

December 25 to January 5 (January 6th is the start of Epiphany.)

Prez Puzzlers

1.
   What U.S. President had the most children?

2.
   Who was the first Roman Catholic President?

3.
   What President was a five-star general?

4.
   Who was the first President to live in the White House?

5.
   Which chief executive had the shortest presidency?

How many consecutive wins did Ken Jennings
have on *Jeopardy*?

84% OF CAT OWNERS ARE WOMEN.

ANSWERS

1.

John Tyler, 15

2.

John F. Kennedy

3.

Dwight D. Eisenhower

4.

John Adams

5.

William Henry Harrison...
He died after only a month in office in 1841.

74

BILL GATES SCORED 1590 ON HIS SATS.

ALTER EGOS

Match the comic strip characters with their alias.

1. Batwoman
2. The Lone Ranger
3. Wonder Woman
4. The Hulk
5. Supergirl
6. Batman
7. Superman
8. Spider-Man
9. Robin
10. Tarzan

(a) Robert Bruce Banner
(b) Peter Parker
(c) Lord Greystoke
(d) John Reid
(e) Clark Kent
(f) Kathy Kane
(g) Dick Grayson
(h) Linda Lee Danvers
(i) Diana Prince
(j) Bruce Wayne

The most common speed limit sign in the United States
is for how many miles per hour?

BEFORE "HELLO" BECAME THE STANDARD
TELEPHONE GREETING, FOLKS SAID "AHOY."
THOMAS EDISON SUGGESTED THE CHANGE.

ANSWERS

1. F
2. D
3. I
4. A
5. H
6. J
7. E
8. B
9. G
10. C

25

❄ SEASONAL STUMPER ❄

If you suffered from pogonophobia,
why might you be afraid of Santa Claus?

Pogonophobia is a fear of beards.

THREE'S COMPANY

1. What sword-bearing trio's motto was "All for one, one for all?"

2. During former President Bill Clinton's youth, he and two other boys formed a sunglass-wearing jazz combo and called themselves what name?

3. Who were Gaspar, Melchior, and Balthasar?

4. What's a turkey in bowling?

5. What group's first movie was *Soup to Nuts?*

What's the name of the dog shown on the Cracker Jack box?

THE FIRST MINIMUM WAGE, INSTITUTED IN THE
U.S. IN 1938, WAS 25 CENTS AN HOUR.

ANSWERS

1.
   The Three Musketeers

2.
   Three Blind Mice

3.
   The Three Wise Men

4.
   Three strikes in a row

5.
   The Three Stooges

Bingo

ACCORDING TO GALLUP, 63% OF
DOGS GET CHRISTMAS PRESENTS FROM
THEIR OWNERS, 58% OF CATS.

COMMAND PERFORMANCE

Fall in line, snap to attention and salute, then answer these questions on command.

1. First, try to beam up the answer to this one: Who were the three main commanders of the starship enterprise in the two *Star Trek* television series?

2. What popular British movie character holds the rank of commander?

3. What general held the rank of Supreme Allied Commander during World War II?

4. Who gave commands aboard Apollo 13?

5. In order to become Commander in Chief of the United States, there are three major considerations. Number one – you must be a natural born citizen of the U.S. Number two – you must be at least 35 years of age. What is number three?

Who was the only U.S. President elected unanimously?

THERE ARE NO PHOTOGRAPHS THAT SHOW
ABRAHAM LINCOLN SMILING.

ANSWERS

1.

Pike, Kirk and Picard

2.

Bond, Commander James Bond

3.

Dwight Eisenhower, later the Commander in Chief

4.

Jim Lovell

5.

Gotcha!- You must be elected!
(unless you're replacing a President removed from office)

George Washington, who ran unopposed both of his terms

ENGLISH MUFFINS WERE FIRST MADE IN
AMERICA, VENETIAN BLINDS WERE INVENTED
BY THE CHINESE, AND BELGIANS WERE
THE FIRST TO MAKE FRENCH FRIES.

DOCTORING IT UP

The answers to each of these clues are doctors.

1.
   It was the pseudonym of author Theodore Geisel.

2.
   Harrison Ford played him in *The Fugitive*.

3.
   Chemist R.S. Lazenby of Waco, Texas invented this in the Old Corner Drug Store in 1885.

4.
   Hugh Laurie plays this free-wheeling, brilliant diagnostician on the FOX TV series.

5.
   This best-selling baby book author won a gold medal in rowing at the 1924 Olympics.

On *Gilligan's Island*, how many people were shipwrecked?

REINDEER ARE SUPERB SWIMMERS.

ANSWERS

1.
   Dr. Seuss

2. Dr. Richard Kimble

3. Dr Pepper (Make no mistake about it –
   There's no period after the "Dr".)

4. Dr. Gregory House, of *House*

5. Dr. Benjamin Spock

7 ("...Gilligan, the Skipper too, the Millionaire, and his Wife, the
Movie Star, the Professor and Mary Ann, here on Gilligan's Isle.")

❄ SEASONAL STUMPER ❄

True or false? In Caracas, Venezuela, it is customary
for people to roller-skate to church on Christmas Eve.

True

FOR BETTER OR WORSE

1. Whose first words to his future wife were, "Miss Todd, I want to dance with you"?

2. How did hearing-plagued inventor Thomas Edison propose to his future wife?

3. "Marriage is an institution, but I'm not ready for an institution yet." What legendary movie queen said it?

4. When actor Tony Perkins married Berinthia Berenson in 1973, who was his best man?

5. What cult religious leader married 2,075 couples in New York's Yankee Stadium in 1982?

George Carlin was the first host of *Saturday Night Live* on October 11th of what year?

THE HUMAN TOOTH HAS APPROXIMATELY
FIFTY MILES OF CANALS IN IT.

ANSWERS

1.

Abraham Lincoln's

2.

In Morse Code – She replied,
"Yes", also in Morse Code.

3.

Mae West

4.

His dog, a pet collie

5.

Reverend Sun Myung Moon (Many of the couples
didn't even know each other!)

1975

FLORIDA'S STATE SONG IS *OLD FOLKS AT HOME*.

MUG SHOTS

1.
Whose face is on the $10,000 bill?

2.
Arrangement in Grey and Black: The Artist's Mother hangs in the Louvre. What mother is portrayed?

3.
Who was the first female to appear on the front of a Wheaties box?

4.
Whose face has appeared on the cover of *TV Guide* the most times?

5.
What happened to the mug of Spanish explorer Balboa, discoverer of the Pacific Ocean, in 1519?

The metal band holding the eraser to the pencil is called a:
a) ferrule b) snype c) clip d) brassard

THE WASHINGTON MONUMENT SINKS
AN AVERAGE OF SIX INCHES A YEAR.

ANSWERS

1.

Salmon P. Chase's

2.

Whistler's mother – That's the original
name of the painting.

3.

Mary Lou Retton

4.

Lucille Ball's

5.

It was taken off. Balboa was accused of treason
and beheaded in Spain.

A

APPROXIMATELY 98% OF ALL COUPONS GO UNUSED.

RED, WHITE AND BLUE

1. He's the editor of the *Daily Planet* in the *Superman* flicks.

2. What big league baseball team changed its name for a while during the Cold War with Russia?

3. What was once painted grey and called the Executive Mansion?

4. By what other name has Broadway been known?

5. The Marcels made what lunar hit in 1961?

How many balls are used in a game of pool?

CANINES WITH THE BEST EYESIGHT?
GREYHOUNDS RULE.

ANSWERS

1.
Perry White

2.
The Cincinnati Reds (as in Soviets)
changed their name to the Red Legs.

3.
The White House

4.
The Great White Way

5.
Blue Moon

16 (including the cue ball)

❄ SEASONAL STUMPER ❄

Robert Louis Stevenson, author of *Treasure Island*,
willed his November 13th birthday to a friend. Why?

Because she disliked her own Christmas birthday.

CATCH PHRASES

Here's a catchy quiz. See how much you know about the words that have caught our ears and been on everyone's lips.

1. What comic got great laughs every time he said, "Would you believe...?"

2. Which restaurant chain had everyone, including Presidential candidates, saying "Where's the beef?"

3. What stomach medicine had people belly-laughing, "I can't believe I ate the whole thing?"

4. In the '70s, millions of people responded to almost anything with "Heeeeyyy!" What TV character started this craze?

5. Which actor became famous for the lines "I'll be back" and "Hasta la vista, baby"?

It was introduced as a beach game called Pretzel. What do we know it as today?

CAESAR SALAD HAS NOTHING TO DO WITH THE RULERS OF ROME. IT WAS FIRST MADE IN A TIJUANA BAR IN THE 1920S.

ANSWERS

1.
Don Adams

2.
Wendy's

3.
Alka-Seltzer

4.
Fonzie on *Happy Days*

5.
Arnold Schwarzenegger

Twister

A SNAKE CAN HEAR WITH ITS TONGUE.

ACRONYMANIA

What do the following stand for?

1. GIGO
2. NECCO
3. ATM
4. SNAFU
5. TCBY
6. CD-ROM
7. YUPPY
8. RPM
9. CAT (Scan)
10. MADD

Just how old was John Glenn when he became
the oldest astronaut to travel in space?

IN 1950, THE TOWN OF HOT SPRINGS, NEW MEXICO,
RENAMED ITSELF TRUTH OR CONSEQUENCES IN
HONOR OF THE GAME SHOW.

ANSWERS

1. Garbage In, Garbage Out
2. New England Confectionary Company
   (as in the candy)
3. Automated Teller Machine
4. Situation Normal All Fouled Up
5. The Country's Best Yogurt
   (originally "This Can't Be Yogurt")
6. Compact Disc – Read Only Memory
7. Young Urban Professional (with a diminutive
   ending as a pet name, e.g. "Johnny")
8. Revolutions Per Minute
9. Computerized Axial Tomography
10. Mothers Against Drunk Driving

77. (A U.S. senator at the time, he flew aboard
the Discovery, which was launched October 29, 1998.)

DOGS CAN UNDERSTAND ABOUT A TWO
HUNDRED WORD HUMAN VOCABULARY, WHILE
CATS COMPREHEND ONLY ABOUT FIFTY WORDS.

Presidential Pooches

1. Named after Bo Diddley, this Portuguese Water Dog is a part of which First Family?

2. True or false? President James Garfield owned a dog named Veto.

3. Gerald Ford's dog, Liberty, gave birth to nine puppies in the White House. What breed was Liberty?

4. Buddy was his pal.

5. Beagle, Little Beagle, Him and Her were the four beagles who sniffed around the White House during whose tenure in the '60s?

The little plastic tips of shoelaces are called:
a) holds b) toppers c) aglets d) fibbers

RED SCHOOLHOUSES WERE PAINTED RED FOR AN ELEMENTARY REASON- IT WAS THE CHEAPEST COLOR.

ANSWERS

1.
"Bo" is a member of the Obamas.

2.
True

3.
Golden retriever

4.
Bill Clinton's

5.
Lyndon Johnson's

C

AN ANT'S SENSE OF SMELL IS JUST
AS GOOD AS A DOG'S.

THE NAME GAME

What's their last name?

1.

   Madonna

2.

   Cher

3.

   Barbie (as in the doll)

4.

   Dorothy (from *The Wizard of Oz*)

5.

   Shakira

How many years of marriage are celebrated
on a Crystal Anniversary?

THE 1,500 POUND LEATHERBACK TURTLE CARRIES
A SHELL THAT IS AS BIG AS A KING SIZE BED- BUT A
LOT HARDER TO FIND FITTED SHEETS FOR!

ANSWERS

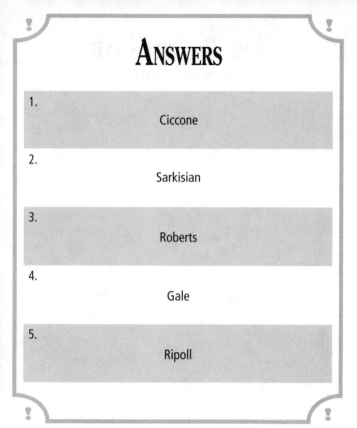

1.
   Ciccone

2.
   Sarkisian

3.
   Roberts

4.
   Gale

5.
   Ripoll

15

❄ SEASONAL STUMPER ❄

What charitable organization revved up its first
Christmas toy drive for needy youngsters in 1947?

Toys for Tots

Minding your P's and Q's

The solutions to these clues all begin with "p" or "q".

1. A statue honoring this naval cartoon hero stands in Crystal City, Texas.

2. This sport bans lefties.

3. It's the airline to Australia.

4. Remove the last four letters of this five-letter word and it's still pronounced the same.

5. A.C. Gilbert, the inventor of the erector set, scaled new heights when he won an Olympic gold medal in 1908 in this event.

He began life as a King and ended up as a U.S. President. Can you identify him?

AN ELEPHANT SMELLS THROUGH ITS MOUTH, NOT ITS TRUNK.

ANSWERS

1.
Popeye

2.
Polo

3.
Qantas

4.
Queue

5.
Pole vault

Gerald Ford, born Leslie King

WHEN OREO COOKIES WERE FIRST MADE, THEY WERE MOUND-SHAPED. THE NAME COMES FROM THE GREEK WORD "OREO", WHICH MEANS "HILL".

WHO SAID IT?

1. "Cross-country skiing is great if you live in a small country."
   a) Steven Wright b) Bob Hope c) Johnny Carson d) Kit Carson

2. "My wife's a water sign. I'm an earth sign.
   Together we make mud."
   a) Regis Philbin b) Rodney Dangerfield c) Jackie Mason d) Perry Mason

3. "Why do they call it rush hour when nothing moves?"
   a) Phyllis Diller b) Robin Williams c) Tom Arnold d) Benedict Arnold

4. "You know you're getting old when
   people tell you how good you look."
   a) Steve Allen b) Bob Hope c) Alan King d) King Kong

5. "I like a woman with a head on her shoulders. I hate necks."
   a) Steve Martin b) Drew Carey c) Norm MacDonald d) Old MacDonald

What product was originally called
Little Short-Cake Fingers?

YOUR NOSE AND EARS NEVER STOP GROWING.

ANSWERS

1.
   A

2.
   B

3.
   B

4.
   C

5.
   A

Twinkies

❄ SEASONAL STUMPER ❄

Why were Animal Crackers designed
with a string handle?

Imported from England to the U.S. in the late 1800s, they were
designed that way so they could be hung on a Christmas tree.

THIS AND THAT

1. What early children's TV show had the young audience seated in the "Peanut Gallery"?

2. Doctors take the Hippocratic Oath. What do nurses take?

3. If you got toy trains for Christmas, where would you find the "crumb box," "bazoo wagon" or the "loose cage"?

4. True or false? Salt dissolves more rapidly in cold water than hot water.

5. The letter "j" appears in the name of how many states in the U.S.?

How many minutes does Minute Rice take to cook?

DR. SEUSS COINED THE TERM "NERD".

ANSWERS

1.
Howdy Doody

2.
The Florence Nightingale Pledge

3.
At the end of the train – Those are other terms for the caboose.

4.
True

5.
Just 1 – New Jersey.

5

GREER GARSON DELIVERED THE LONGEST ACCEPTANCE SPEECH EVER IN THE HISTORY OF THE ACADEMY AWARDS WHEN SHE WON THE OSCAR FOR BEST ACTRESS IN *MRS. MINIVER*. HER SPEECH LASTED THIRTY MINUTES.

African-Americans

1.
Who was the first African-American NBA coach?

2.
What comedienne/actress was born Caryn Johnson?

3.
Can you name the singer who was the original host of the music and dance show *Solid Gold*?

4.
He won an Oscar as Best Actor for 1963's *Lilies of the Field* and she won likewise for her performance in 2002's *Monster's Ball*.

5.
What was Muhammad Ali's name when he first became heavyweight champ in 1964?

What's the most popular first name for a U.S. President?

THE WORD "KARATE" MEANS "EMPTY HAND".

ANSWERS

1. Bill Russell – He became player/coach of the Boston Celtics in 1966.

2. Whoopi Goldberg

3. Dionne Warwick

4. Sidney Poitier and Halle Berry

5. Cassius Marcellus Clay

James – There were six – Madison, Monroe, Polk, Buchanan, Garfield, and Carter.

IF YOU THINK YOU EAT LIKE A BIRD, THINK AGAIN.
BIRDS EAT FROM ONE QUARTER TO ONE HALF
THEIR BODY WEIGHT EVERY DAY.

ALL OVER THE MAP

1. What do Ada, Kansas, Ama, Louisiana, Anna, Illinois, Oto, Iowa, and Pep, New Mexico have in common? (Hint: You'll be back and forth on this one.)

2. True or False? Texas is nicknamed the Lone Star State because of the star in the center of its flag.

3. What California town was named after its movie studios?

4. Can you name the city which is known as the Athens of the South because of its many educational institutions and buildings in the Greek classical style?

5. What state is nicknamed the Land of 10,000 Lakes?

When ESPN announced its list of the 50 greatest athletes of all time, what was the name of the only non-human to make the grade?

THE AVERAGE GARDEN VARIETY CATERPILLAR HAS 228 MUSCLES IN ITS HEAD.

ANSWERS

1.
The towns' names are all palindromes, words that read the same backward or forward.

2.
True

3.
Paramount

4.
Nashville, Tennessee... Of course, it's also known as the Music City.

5.
Minnesota- which actually has 22,000 lakes. (Incidentally, the NBA's Los Angeles Lakers originally played in Minneapolis- hence, the team name.)

Secretariat

❄ SEASONAL STUMPER ❄

What was the name of the 12-year-old boy who sang the hit tune, *I Saw Mommy Kissing Santa Claus*?

Jimmy Boyd

ALL IN THE FAMILY

*Everything is relative here with
these questions about famous folk.*

1.
Who is Rhea Perlman's husband?

2. A singing superstar and a song legend's daughter were married in a civil ceremony in the Dominican Republic on May 26, 1994. Name them.

3. True or false? If his grandfather hadn't changed the family's last name, famed aviator Charles Lindbergh would have been known as Charles Manson.

4. The mother of Mariska Hargitay, co-star of television's *Law and Order: Special Victims Unit*, was one of Hollywood's great blonde bombshells. Who was she?

5.
Who is Charlie Sheen's older brother?

Who won the most gold medals in a single Olympic Games?

VAN GOGH SIGNED HIS PAINTINGS WITH
HIS FIRST NAME, VINCENT.

ANSWERS

1.
   Danny DeVito

2.
   Michael Jackson and Lisa Marie Presley

3.
   True

4.
   Jayne Mansfield

5.
   Emilio Estevez

Michael Phelps (eight, in 2008)

❄ SEASONAL STUMPER ❄

What are the two busiest
shopping days of the year?

The Friday and Saturday before Christmas

It's Not Whether you Win or Lose, But How you Host the Game

Name the original host (or only host) of the following TV game shows.

1.
   Jeopardy!

2.
   Hollywood Squares

3.
   Who Wants to be a Millionaire?

4.
   Deal or No Deal

5.
   The Newlywed Game

What's the plural of the word moose?

LIFE SAVERS ARE THE BEST-SELLING CANDY
IN THE WORLD.

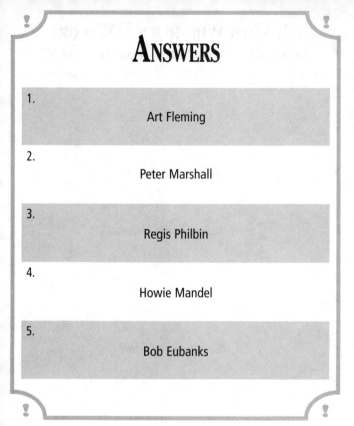

ANSWERS

1.
Art Fleming

2.
Peter Marshall

3.
Regis Philbin

4.
Howie Mandel

5.
Bob Eubanks

Moose

WEST POINT ORIGINATED CLASS RINGS IN 1835.

Time and Time Again

1. What is the third hand on a clock called?

2. An extremely odd happenstance occurred in 1978 on the 6th of May at 12:34 p.m. Do you know what it was?

3. True or false? Any month that starts on a Sunday will have a Friday the 13th.

4. If a centennial relates to a period of 100 years, to what does a decennial relate?

5. How many seconds are there in a leap year?

What does EPCOT stand for?

A STACK OF A TRILLION NEW ONE-DOLLAR BILLS WOULD REACH 69,000 MILES HIGH.

ANSWERS

1.

The second hand

2.

At that exact moment, the time read 12:34, 5/6/78.

3.

True

4.

A period of 10 years

5.

31,622,400

Experimental Prototype Community of Tomorrow

❄ SEASONAL STUMPER ❄

In what country is the Christmas gift-giver
a kindly old witch named La Befana?

Italy

BIRTHDAY BAFFLERS

1. Who said, "I don't get respect from anyone. My twin brother forgot my birthday."

2. What famous poet/writer was expelled from West Point because he showed up for a parade in his birthday suit?

3. Mildred and Patty Hill are in the musical history books for what reason?

4. What holiday-related thing do Sissy Spacek, Jimmy Buffett, and Barbara Mandrell have in common?

5. Dinah Shore was only 19 when she died, yet had an entertainment career which spanned more than 60 years. How so?

Who was born Marshall Mathers III?

YANKEE DOODLE WAS COMPOSED IN ENGLAND AS AN ANTI-AMERICAN TUNE.

ANSWERS

1.

Rodney Dangerfield

2.

Edgar Allan Poe

3.

They wrote *Happy Birthday to You.*

4.

They share the same birthday, December 25.

5.

She was born in a leap year, on February 29, 1916.

Eminem

STAN LAUREL WAS MARRIED EIGHT TIMES;
HOWEVER, HE ONLY HAD FOUR WIVES.

HORSEPLAY

1.

He was horse racing's last Triple Crown winner.

2.

What's the longest amount of letters
a racing horse can have in its name?

3.

By the way, what is a farrier?

4.

What "first" occurred when it left St. Joseph,
Missouri, on April 3, 1860?

5.

What's the drink du jour of the Kentucky Derby?

What building is on the back of a five-dollar bill?

A WOMAN CAN TALK WITH LESS EFFORT THAN A MAN
BECAUSE HER VOCAL CHORDS ARE SHORTER.

ANSWERS

1.
Affirmed, in 1978

2.
Eighteen

3.
A horse shoer… There are some
15,000 farriers in the U.S.

4.
The first Pony Express

5.
Mint julep

The Lincoln Memorial

❄ SEASONAL STUMPER ❄

What's the most commonly played song on
the radio during the Christmas season?

Jingle Bells … Second is *White Christmas.*

MOTHERS OF INVENTION

1.
What invention was originally called the "Epsicle?"

2.
What inventor holds the most patents?

3.
What is it that Daisuke Inoue invented in 1971?
(Hint: Think *Sing Along With Mitch*.)

4.
Ermal Cleon Fraze went on a family picnic in 1959, but forgot to bring a can opener, forcing him to use his car bumper to open the can. It later inspired him to invent what useful device?

5.
Who invented charcoal briquettes?

What is the equivalent of 5:45 P.M. in military hours?

THE WORD "AMEN" IS SPOKEN IN MORE TONGUES THAN ANY OTHER WORD.

ANSWERS

1. The popsicle.... Invented by 11-year-old Frank Epperson when he accidentally left a glass of punch with a stick in it on his porch overnight, he renamed it when applying for the patent, reportedly because his kids referred to the ice delight as "Pop's sicle."

2. Thomas Edison, of course... The Wizard of Menlo Park holds 1,093 patents.

3. The karaoke machine

4. The pop-top can opener

5. It's none other than automobile pioneer Henry Ford.

1745

❄ SEASONAL STUMPER ❄

In the Christmas carol *The Twelve Days of Christmas*, what is the fourth day's gift?

If you said, "Four calling birds," you're wrong. They are "collied birds" (black birds). Oh, and about the fifth day's gift: the five golden rings are ringed pheasants, not jewelry.

THE DEAN'S LIST

1.
A pitcher, he was a 30-game winner for the 1934 St. Louis Cardinals. Name him.

2.
He was called Watergate's "master manipulator of the cover up" by the FBI.

3.
This democratic polico's critics sometimes labeled his youthful supporters "Deanie Babies".

4.
In the farcical movie *Animal House*, this man was determined to expel the Delta House Fraternity.

5.
Big Bad John was a big, big hit for this recording artist in 1961.

What do you call a group of swans?

WOODPECKERS DON'T GET HEADACHES.

ANSWERS

1. Dizzy Dean

2. John Dean

3. Howard Dean

4. Dean Vernon Wormer

5. Jimmy Dean

A bevy

IF THE WIRE OF A SLINKY WAS LAID OUT FLAT,
IT WOULD MEASURE 87 FEET.

JACK OF ALL TRADES

1. He hosted the *Tonight Show* before Johnny Carson.

2. This comedy veteran was the star of the one-man Broadway show, *Politically Incorrect*.

3. Born Benjamin Kubelsky, this comedian grew up in Waukegan, Illinois.

4. His number "42" was retired permanently by Major League Baseball.

5. You'll find twelve of them on the four of them in a deck of them. Identify "them".

How many dots, or pips as they are called, are there on a pair of dice?

COCA COLA WAS BANNED FROM INDIA IN 1977 FOR REFUSING TO DISCLOSE ITS SECRET FORMULA.

ANSWERS

1.

Jack Paar

2.

Jackie Mason

3.

Jack Benny

4.

Jackie Robinson

5. There are twelve eyes on the four jacks in a deck of cards (two one-eyed jacks shown right side up and upside down and a pair of two-eyed jacks, also shown right side up and upside down).

42

AMERICANS SAY THEIR FAVORITE COLOR IS BLUE, BUT THE MOST POPULAR CAR AND HOUSE COLOR IS WHITE.

CANDYLAND

1.

Who is the Baby Ruth candy bar named after?

2.

How about M&M's?

3.

What chocolate, chewy candy did Austrian Leo Hirshfield bring to the U.S. in 1896?

4.

"Taste the Rainbow" is the slogan of what candy?

5.

What brand of Life Savers is known to produce bright sparks when bitten in a dark room?

This game was invented by Chris Haney and Scott Abbott on a rainy Montreal Saturday in 1979.

ACCORDING TO AN INTELLIGENCE TEST OF 79 DOG BREEDS, THE SMARTEST IS THE BORDER COLLIE.

ANSWERS

1.
No, not for Babe Ruth, but for Ruth Cleveland, the daughter of President Grover Cleveland.

2.
M&M's, first sold in 1941, were named for their developers, Forrest Mars and Bruce Murries.

3.
The Tootsie Roll

4.
Skittles

5.
Wint-O-Green

Trivial Pursuit

THE REAL NAME OF EDDIE, THE SCRAPPY
DOG ON TV'S *FRASIER*, WAS MOOSE
(WHO, AT 16, DIED OF OLD AGE IN 2006).

HODGEPODGE

1. See if you can clean up on this one…
   What word has consecutive u's?

2. At what store did Wal-Mart founder
   Sam Walton get his first job?

3. What happy icon did Harvey Ball create in 1963?

4. Who is known in Latin as Michael Musculus?

5. Who was the first President to ride in a car, fly in a
   plane and go underwater in a submarine?

National Pi Day falls on what day of March?

FOR SOME UNKNOWN REASON, A DUCK'S
QUACK DOESN'T ECHO.

ANSWERS

1.

Vacuum

2.

JC Penney

3.

The Smiley Face

4.

Mickey Mouse

5.

Teddy Roosevelt... And, no doubt, they
were all rough rides.

14 (The real "Pi" moments occur
March 14, at 1:59 – or 3/14 1:59 a.m. and p.m.)

**IF YOU HAD A LINE OF DIMES 113.6 MILES LONG,
YOU'D BE A MILLIONAIRE!**

TRIVIQUATION

Test your math and your trivia wits here. Fill in the number portion of the answers suggested by the clues and then perform the arithmetic to solve the Triviquation.

Players on a lacrosse team _____ .

Points for a touchdown − _____ .

Strings on a violin x _____ .

Letters in Greek alphabet − _____ .

Times Ford was elected U.S. President = _____ .

What state has the most electoral votes?

ACCORDING TO THE KLEENEX PEOPLE, THE AVERAGE PERSON BLOWS HIS NOSE 256 TIMES A YEAR.

ANSWERS

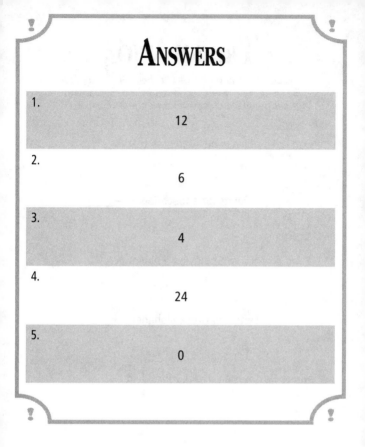

1.

12

2.

6

3.

4

4.

24

5.

0

California – 55

THE FRENCH CALL COTTON CANDY "PAPA'S BREAD".

THE FEAR OF IT

Combine the word with the phobia it describes.

1. Astraphobia

(a) Fear of public speaking

2. Cynophobia

(b) Fear of mice

3. Glossophobia

(c) Fear of computers (or machines)

4. Musophobia

(d) Fear of dogs

5. Logizomechanophobia

(e) Fear of lightning and thunder

Which nation has maintained a zero birth rate for many years?

PHILADELPHIA ORIGINATED THE SYSTEM OF EVEN-NUMBERED RESIDENCES ON ONE SIDE OF THE STREET AND ODD NUMBERED HOMES ON THE OTHER SIDE.

Answers

1.
   E

2.
   D

3.
   A

4.
   B

5.
   C

Vatican City

LIFE SAVERS CANDY WAS INVENTED THE
SAME YEAR THE TITANIC SANK.

FACT OR FIB?

1.
Gone with the Wind was Margaret Mitchell's only novel.

2. The Holland Tunnel, connecting New York City and New Jersey under the Hudson River, is named after the nationality of Manhattan's first colonists.

3. Columbia, Harvard, Yale and Princeton were the original four schools in a college athletic league. The Roman numeral for four is IV, so they decided to call themselves the "Ivy" League.

4. The weight of whales is measured on a Saffin-Simpson scale.

5. Polar bears can outrun reindeer.

In 2005, what became a dictionary word meaning "to obtain information about on the World Wide Web"?

YES, LIMA BEANS DO COME FROM LIMA. THEY WERE BROUGHT HERE FROM PERU BY U.S. NAVY CAPTAIN JOHN HARRIS IN 1824.

ANSWERS

1.

FACT

2.
FIB- It's named after the engineer who directed the tunnel-building operation, Clifford Milburn Holland.

3.

FACT

4.
FIB- If you missed this one it's a real natural disaster. Hurricanes are measured on the Saffin-Simpson scale. (By the way, the Moby Dicks of the world are sized up at whale-weigh stations. Ho! Ho! Ho!)

5.

FACT

Google

❄ <u>SEASONAL STUMPER</u> ❄

Who named the Chipmunks in their 1958 *Chipmunks Christmas Song*?

Performer and songwriter David Seville... Alvin and Simon were named for two executives at Liberty Records, Al Bennett and Simon Waronker. Theodore was named for the recording engineer, Ted Keep.

Tube Test

1. Name the late-night TV host who previously worked as a writer and producer for *The Simpsons*.

2. What does *M*A*S*H* stand for?

3. Who was the first woman to host *Saturday Night Live*?

4. What's the longest running television show of all-time?

5. Name the American reality TV program created by Charlie Parsons in 1992 and first made as a Swedish show called *Expedition: Robinson*.

What is Tiger Woods' real first name?

NEOPHOBIA IS THE FEAR OF ANYTHING NEW.

ANSWERS

1.

Conan O'Brien

2.

Mobile Army Surgical Hospital

3.

Candice Bergen

4.

Meet the Press... It began in 1947.

5.

Survivor

Eldrick

THE INTERNATIONAL LINT MUSEUM
IS IN RUTLAND, VERMONT.

HARDBALL TRIVIA

Ol' St. Nick's not just a statistical freak. He loves odd and unusual facts about the national pastime. See how many of them you know.

1. How many feet is it from home plate to second base on a major league diamond?

2. What's the score of a forfeited big league game?

3. Can a pitcher's glove be green?

4. Where is the Little League World Series played?

5. How about the College World Series?

What nickname did Charles Gillett, the President of the New York City Convention and Visitors Bureau, coin?

A CHILD'S BELIEF IN SANTA CLAUS PEAKS AT AGE 4.

ANSWERS

1.

127 feet, 3 3/8 inches

2.

9-0

3.

Yes… It may be any solid color except white or gray.

4.

Williamsport, Pennsylvania

5.

Omaha, Nebraska

The Big Apple

❄ SEASONAL STUMPER ❄

Who sang *Jingle Bell Rock*?

Bobby Helms

The Funny Pages

1. "We have met the enemy and he is us," is the most famous line of the title character created by Walt Kelly. Do you know the comic strip?

2. Joe Shuster and Jerry Siegel created what superhero?

3. Who is Charlie Brown's favorite baseball player?

4. Who created *Doonesbury*?

5. Where does Batman live?

Name the classic TV comedy that began with the theme song *You're My Greatest Love*.

BENJAMIN FRANKLIN WAS THE FIRST TO SAY,
"AN APPLE A DAY KEEPS THE DOCTOR AWAY."

ANSWERS

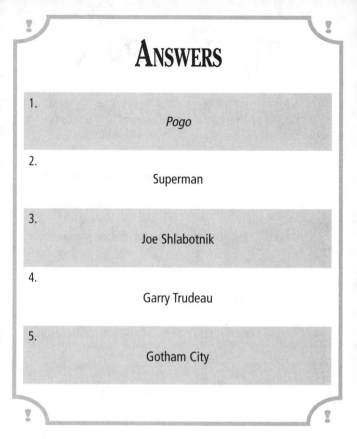

1.
Pogo

2.
Superman

3.
Joe Shlabotnik

4.
Garry Trudeau

5.
Gotham City

The Honeymooners – The song was written by Jackie Gleason.

IN AUGUST 1911, VINCENZO PERUGGIA, AN EMPLOYEE OF THE LOUVRE MUSEUM, STOLE THE *MONA LISA*. HE KEPT THE PAINTING FOR TWO YEARS BUT WAS ARRESTED WHEN HE TRIED TO SELL IT.

THE ALMIGHTY DOLLAR

1. The one dollar bill is the most frequently circulated paper currency in the U.S. What's second?

2. True or false? There are 293 ways to make change for a dollar.

3. Whose portrait is on the $50 bill and, for an extra helping of plum pudding, what building is pictured on the flip side?

4. Who was the first American billionaire?

5. In 1999, John Carpenter became the first person to win a million bucks on what television show?

What's the only word that ends in "sede"?

CHINESE CHECKERS WAS INVENTED IN ENGLAND IN THE 1800S AND WAS ORIGINALLY CALLED "HALMA".

ANSWERS

1.

The $20 bill

2.

True

3.

U.S. Grant is on the front, the U.S. Capitol is on the back.

4.

Standard Oil founder John D. Rockefeller, in 1911

5.

Who Wants to Be a Millionaire?

Supersede

❄ SEASONAL STUMPER ❄

What holiday item do the states of Oregon, Michigan, Wisconsin, Pennsylvania and North Carolina lead the nation in producing?

Christmas trees